Richard Scarry's
THINGS TO KNOW

CARNIVAL

GETTING READY
FOR SCHOOL

"It is time to get up for school,"
said Huckle's mother.
"Why do I have to go to school?"
asked Huckle.
"All children go to school to
learn how to read and write."

Huckle got up.
He yawned and rubbed
the sleep out of
his eyes.

He washed his face with
soap and warm water.

He brushed his teeth.

toothpaste

He combed his hair
with cold water.

comb

Then Huckle got
dressed.

That is NOT the way
to put on your
trousers, Huckle!

cap

braces

shirt

jacket

underpants

sand-shoes

shoes

socks

Mother Cat gave hot cereal to Huckle
for his breakfast.

bowl
teapot
cup
sauce
briefcase
tableclo

Lowly Worm called in on his way to school. "Hurry,

Mother Cat walked with Huckle
to the school bus stop.
Honk! Honk.
The school bus came
to take the children
to school

fork   knife   spoon

or you will be late for school," he said.

bell

This is Huckle's classroom.
Behind the big desk sits Miss Honey,
his teacher.

teacher

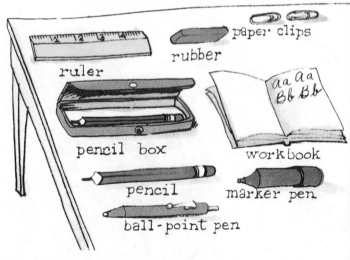

paper clips

rubber

ruler

pencil box

workbook

pencil

marker pen

ball-point pen

calendar

SEPTEMBER

SUN	MON	TUES	WED	THU	FRI	SAT
		1	2	3	4	5
6	7	8	9	10	11	12
13	14	15	16	17	18	19
20	21	22	23	24	25	26
27	28	29	30			

$2 + 1 = 3$

$2 +$

pencil sharpener

paste pot

blackboard
duster

scissors

chalk

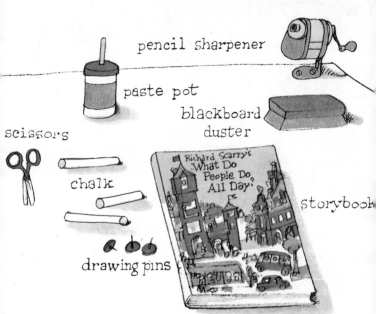

Richard Scarry's
What Do
People Do
All Day?

storybook

drawing pins

Each day, Miss Honey
teaches her class
something new.

Today, she is going to teach them the alphabet.
Do YOU know the alphabet?
It's a good thing to learn.

LEARNING NUMBERS

1

2

3

4

5

6

Do you know how to count?
I'll bet you do!
Can you count how many
pirates there are?

7

8

9

10

THE PLAYGROUND

Everybody is doing something.

What do you think is most fun?

rings

sliding-pole

stilts

pat·a·cake

spade

pail

sand box

ring

tag

skipping-rope

7 8

6

4 5

leap-frog

3

hop scotch

2

1

PETROL

petrol
pump

petrol
storage
tank

GARDENER

OIL

AT THE FILLING STATION

At the busy, busy filling station, all kinds of
trucks come in to get oil and petrol. The
attendants haven't even had time to cover up
the new underground storage tank.
What do you think the carpenter is going to
build with all that wood?

MACHINES

Machines help people to do their work.

Eli Cottontail picks cotton balls with his cotton-picker.

Big heavy rocks are loaded into the rock-crusher.

combine harvester

Farmer Pig gathers his crop with a harvesting-machine.

wheat grain

crusher

These road-builders use many different machines to build a road.

The grader makes the ground smooth

ditch digger

Digger Dog is digging a ditch for the big water pipe.

The bulldozer
moves earth

The mobile crane
lifts heavy things.

AT THE AIRPORT

Father Cat took Huckle and Little Sister to the airport. Rudolf, the famous pilot, showed them how a plane works.

tail

rudder

elevator

fuselage

aileron

wing

helicopter

wind indicator

cockpit

propeller

nose

a mechanic
checking the engine

THE HARBOUR

Here is a busy harbour full of boats. Who likes to sail in a glass boat?

Lowly Worm!

quay

motor boat

racer

lifeboat

B

bridge

portholes

Tug

rowing-boat

speed-boat

bottle

HELP!

gangplank

jetty

signal
flag

rope

submarine

ly
m

COLOURS

RED

fire engine

heart

strawberry

apple

the inside o
a watermelo

Drawing and painting are always fur
Can you name all the colours? Try.

Arthur Pig paints a
red apple on the pape

paint

water

ORANGE
Daddy Pig paints his boat orange.

orange

goldfish

pumpkin

carrot

bus

YELLOW

Yellow is a bright,
sunny colour.
Can you name all the
things that are
yellow.

banana

daffodil

sweetcorn

be

lemon

chees

peas

leaf

blades of grass

lettuce

pine tree

clover leaf

GREEN

Many things that grow are green. Huckle painted the car green. Now he has green paint all over himself.

BLUE

easel

Big Hilda's favourite colour is blue. What colour do you think she is going to paint her drawing? What colour would YOU paint it?

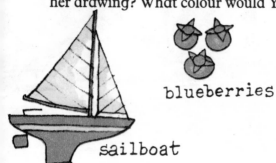

sailboat

blueberries

bluebell

PURPLE

Purple is almost the same colour as violet.

violet

plum

pansy

thistle

grapes

BROWN

walnut

potato

shoelace

chocolate
Easter Bun

Colours can be light or dark,
A potato is light brown.
A chocolate Easter bunny
is dark brown.
Huckle mixes red and black to g
brown paint.

red   black

BLACK

liquorice sweet

doorbell

hat

tyre

black

white

Black is the opposite of white.

egg

snowman

Carnival
An imprint of the Children's Division
of the Collins Publishing Group
8 Grafton Street, London W1X 3LA

Published by Carnival 1988

ISBN 0 00 194434 7

Printed & bound in Great Britain by
PURNELL BOOK PRODUCTION LIMITED
A MEMBER OF BPCC plc